see Christ in Christmas

12 symbols of Christmas

written by
Melissa Sunday

illustrated by
Alyssa Parker

*For Brandon, Blake, Evelyn, Oliver, Eli, &
my angel mother, who taught me to love life*

Text copyright © 2021 Melissa King Sunday
Illustrations copyright © 2021 by Alyssa Stromberg Parker

All rights reserved. Printed in China.

ISBN 978-0-578-71852-1

Visit us at *SoFestive.com*

During the Christmas season
Special symbols fill the earth.
Each one will help you remember
The importance of Jesus' birth.

He is the Son of God—the Savior.
He brings meaning to this life.
This season will be more wonderful
When in Christmas you see Christ.

star

First is the star
That shines sparkly and bright.
It will remind you of Christ's birth
On that first Christmas night.

The wise men followed the new star
To the babe born in Bethlehem.
You, too, can follow Christ's light in your life
And be wise just like them.

candy cane

Candy canes are shaped like a J—
The beginning of Jesus' name.
Their red and white stripes will help you
Remember the reasons He came.

Red is a symbol of the blood
Jesus shed in Gethsemane.
White represents His sinless life,
His faith, and purity.

Just as the shepherds of old used a crook
To guide their precious sheep,
Christ is your Good Shepherd, too.
He'll lead you to safety and peace.

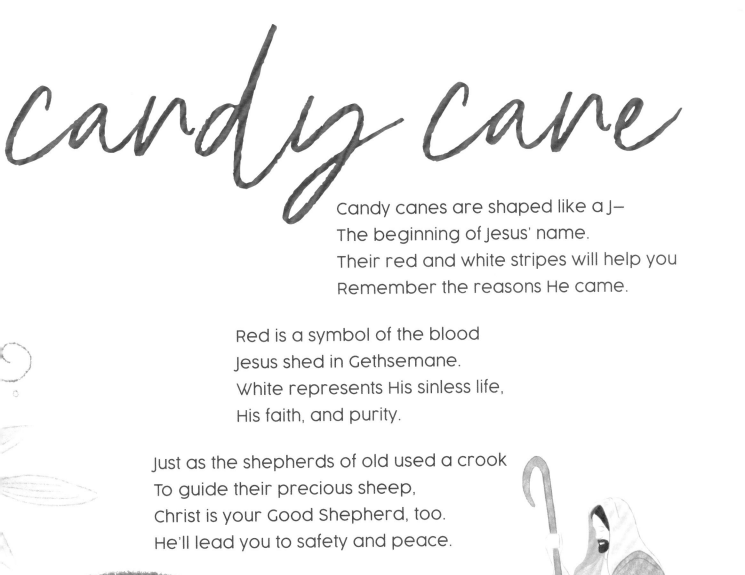

jingle bells

When you hear the sound of jingle bells
Ringing through the air,
Think of the angels in heaven
That announced Christ's birth with care.

They said, "Glory to God in the Highest
And on earth peace, good will toward men."
Bells will help you remember the praises
Of angels rejoicing in heav'n.

poinsettia

Poinsettias come from Mexico.
Their leaves look like a star.
This flower will help you remember
The wise men who came from afar.

The color red will help you think
Of the blood that Jesus spilt.
His loving sacrifice can erase your sins,
Your sadness, and your guilt.

snowflake

No two snowflakes are alike.
Yes, this is the truth.
Each six-sided icy creation
Symbolizes Christ's love for you.

Everyone is special to Him.
Everyone is unique.
Don't look for the world's attention—
Only His approval you should seek.

Unlike the snowflake, remember this—
His love for you will never melt.
Because of Christ's birth and sacrifice,
His love and your worth can always be felt.

presents

Each time you see a present
Wrapped and tied with string,
Remember the greatest gift of all
Is your Savior, Lord, and King.

The wise men gave Jesus gifts
Of frankincense, gold, and myrrh.
But all that Christ wants from you
Is your heart—kind, true, and pure.

lights

Long ago, there were no such things
As electric Christmas lights.
Candles were placed gently on branches
To light up trees on wintry nights.

You no longer need burning candles
To make your trees shine bright.
But when you see a candle glowing,
Remember that Jesus is the true light.

angels

Angels played a special part
In the first Christmas story.
One came to Mary, young and fair,
To prepare her heart to receive His glory.

Another visited the shepherds
And told them not to fear.
The angel brought good tidings of joy—
Christ was born in a stable near!

There are still angels among you
Who will help you feel God's love.
Never forget they are here to help
And guide you from up above.

stocking

Legend says there were three poor daughters
Who each needed money to become a wife.
St. Nicholas secretly put gold in their socks
So they could begin their married life.

Stockings will help you remember
To look for ways to help others.
And that Jesus was the greatest example
Of serving your sisters and brothers.

wreath

Christmas wreaths are pretty and round
With no beginning or end.
They represent eternity
Made possible by Christ, your friend.

Each time you see a festive wreath
Hanging proudly on a door,
Remember the wonderful gift you have
To live forevermore.

evergreen trees

Christmas trees are evergreen.
They never turn dingy and brown.
Because of Christ, eternal life is possible
For you and all those around.

As you keep Him as your focus,
You show your gratitude, and your love.
This is like the top of the tree—
Always reaching to heaven above.

dove

A dove is a beautiful, gentle, white bird
That symbolizes peace on earth.
This peace is available to all mankind
Because of Christ's humble birth.

If you turn to Jesus Christ
No matter what comes your way,
You will feel true peace always
And not just on Christmas day.

meet the makers

Melissa King Sunday, Author

Melissa is a holiday enthusiast who loves celebrating life with her husband and four children. When she isn't decorating for a party, you can find her soaking up the sunshine, hiking in the great outdoors, planning the next family getaway, or proudly playing Christmas music in July.

She gets her brown hair and big cheeks from her mom, Marilyn, who passed away from cancer. In her honor, Melissa created SoFestive.com to inspire others to create a happy life with those they love. Her simple holiday, party, and family-fun ideas have been featured in both local and national media networks. But perhaps her greatest accomplishment is that her children know when Pie Day is.

 @ sofestive   / sofestive   sofestive.com

Alyssa Stromberg Parker, Illustrator

Alyssa, a Freelance Illustrator/Designer, received her bachelor's degree at Brigham Young University in a limited enrollment Visual Arts program, specializing in Illustration. While this is her first illustrated book, her work can be seen in magazines, websites, manuals and brand designs. She and her husband, Dalin, have two children, and reside in Nashville, Tennessee. She loves caring for her kids full-time while living her dream of Freelancing.

  @lyss.and.company   / lyss.and.company   lyssandcompany.com